SPOTLIGHT ON BLENDS

Book Two

End
Consonant Blends

Book Two
End
Consonant Blends

First edition published by
The Robinswood Press 1997
Reprinted 1999

Designed by
Catalyst Ltd   Stourbridge   England

Printed by Wynstones Press

The Robinswood Press

Stourbridge   England

ISBN 1-869981-561

CONTENTS

Page

FOREWORD

Like most busy enthusiastic teachers, I am always interested to see what new resource material is available to help those pupils who require extra attention for specific difficulties. Gillian Aitken's first book *"Spotlight on Words"* has proved very popular with my students and has provided an enjoyable way of reinforcing phonic sounds in a user-friendly format. The pupils are having fun while working on a particular area that requires additional strengthening.

The criteria that are particularly important to me in selecting resource material are:

- good, clear print.
- an uncluttered layout.
- variety.
- a high interest level without being gimmicky.
- work that is challenging but not too daunting.
- worksheets that cover just one specific point for use alongside a structured teaching programme.
- work that has a high interest level for older pupils too.
- clear guidelines on how to use the resources.

Gillian Aitken's latest contribution *"Spotlight on Blends"* again meets these criteria. It will therefore be a valuable addition to the resource material for both the specialist and class teacher to use alongside material already available and to provide reinforcement of sounds already taught and skills such as scanning, tracking and visual discrimination.

Pat Denham
SEN Teacher Elmfield Steiner School and VI Specialist Teacher with Sandwell MBC.

Pat Denham, BPhil, Cert Ed, is a teacher with extensive teaching experience in both the State and independent sectors and across a wide age range of pupils. Her work includes Class Teaching in a Steiner school and Special Needs teaching, especially for visually impaired pupils, throughout the educational spectrum.

ABOUT THE AUTHOR

Gillian Aitken MA, PGCE, RSA Dip. TEFL, AMBDA

Gillian Aitken trained originally as an English teacher, and taught in schools for a number of years. More recently she has concentrated on areas in teaching English where a specialised approach is required. These have included teaching English to pupils with Special Needs, teaching pupils where English is a Second or Foreign Language, and adult literacy work with the Dyslexia Institute.

Ms Aitken therefore has a unique range of experience gained practically both in Britain and abroad, and through further academic study. This background has provided her with perfect opportunities to develop a variety of exercises - such as the blend exercises in both these *"Spotlight on Blends"* titles, and the wordsearch exercises in her first and now well-renowned publication with The Robinswood Press - *"Spotlight on Words"*. All these exercises meet the educationalist's requirement to build spelling and reading skills whilst the pupil becomes engrossed in the challenge and enjoyment of the exercises themselves.

Ms Aitken lives in Sussex and is an Associate Member of the British Dyslexia Association. She continues to work as a specialist English teacher.

INTRODUCTION

"Spotlight on Blends" Book Two aims to give systematic practice of consonant blends at the end of words, and thus complements *Book One*, which focuses on initial consonant blends. As pointed out in the Introduction to *Book One*, consonant blends are an essential part of our spelling system and their high frequency means that they should be an integral part of any structured literacy programme. End blends in particular cause problems for younger pupils learning to read and write, while dyslexic pupils of all ages need constant practice and reinforcement of end blends since they tend to omit one of the elements of sounds contained within the blend. The worksheets contained in *"Spotlight on Blends" Book Two* will provide a useful resource for the busy teacher following a phonetic approach to reading and spelling. The easier worksheets are suitable for pupils in the early stages of a literacy programme, while the more demanding sheets assume a more developed linguistic awareness and are designed for older pupils. The order in which the worksheets are used will depend entirely on the structured programme which the teacher is following and the individual needs of pupils.

End blends fall into the following general categories:

i)   Blends containing the /s/ phoneme, for example, 'st', 'sk' and 'sp'.

ii)   Those with a nasal sound as one element, for example, 'mp', 'nd', 'nt', 'nk', 'nch', 'nge' and 'nce'. (The ending 'ng' is treated as a blend in this book due to its visual and sound similarity to other blends in this group, although it is actually a consonant digraph as only one sound is made by these letters.)

iii)   Blends with the sound /l/ such as 'ld', 'lt', 'lk', 'lf' and 'lve'.

iv)   Blends ending in the sound /t/, for example, 'ft', 'ct' and 'pt'.

All these blends are given systematic practice in *"Spotlight on Blends" Book Two*. Each blend is given a separate focus before being contrasted with a similar sounding blend. Blends of very high frequency such as 'st' or 'nk' are presented in a variety of worksheets at different levels of difficulty, allowing for a great deal of consolidation. For example, there are 10 worksheets focusing on 'st' either separately or contrasted with 'sk' or 'sp'. (Blends such as 'st' or 'sk' which can be found on both initial or final position are also featured in *"Spotlight on Blends" Part One*.)

The worksheets are varied in format, and aim to develop different skills. Research has shown that developing phonological awareness leads to improved reading accuracy and spelling. There is therefore a strong emphasis, especially in the easier worksheets, on tasks which develop this awareness. These include exercises which involve blending the beginning of words (the 'onset') with the remaining chunk (the 'rime'); choosing the correct short vowel to finish words; blending beginning, middle and end sounds to make words; blending syllables; and various rhyming tasks. Some worksheets require the pupil to identify nonsense words, a task which forces him/her to decode phonologically without the aid of visual recall.

However, other skill areas are also focused on in the various worksheets. Very often words with the target blend are presented in a meaningful linguistic context, and tasks which require the pupil to insert missing words into sentences, or to match target words with meanings, aim to extend vocabulary and develop comprehension skills. The majority of the worksheets, even those at a more basic level, present language in context, so that pupils are practising both reading and spelling skills. In some worksheets pupils are required to write their own sentences, while in many cases sentences used in worksheets can be used for dictation as an optional follow-up to give further practice of the target blend.

Dyslexic pupils have visual sequencing difficulties as well as sound processing problems, so some worksheets focus on visual discrimination exercises, for example, word-tracking in a line of letters or wordsearch activities.

Grammatical awareness is also encouraged in some worksheets which focus on prefixes or suffixes, or those which make specific references to parts of speech such as nouns or verbs. For example, longer words ending in 'ance' or 'ence' are nouns, and Worksheets 43 and 44 require pupils to change related verbs or adjectives to nouns ending in the target blend.

The layout of the worksheets is designed to be as clear and uncluttered as possible, enabling pupils to work independently if necessary, or with minimum help from the teacher. Where blends are used contrastively, the use of coloured pens is suggested to highlight the different sounds. This is particularly recommended for tasks which require the completion of words by choosing the correct end blend (for example, Worksheets 7 and 8).

Detailed teaching notes to accompany each worksheet are to be found in the rear section of the book after the worksheets. These include suggestions about using the worksheets, and possible areas of difficulty where the pupil might need guidance, or where ambiguity might arise. Answers are included where appropriate. Phonetic symbols have not been used to describe sounds in the teaching notes as it is assumed that most teachers will not be familiar with these symbols. A sound is represented by the letter names inside slanted brackets, for example, /st/, while a spelling choice is indicated by inverted commas, for example, 'st'. Long vowel sounds are indicated by the diacritic ¯ above the vowel, while short vowels are indicated by the diacritic ˇ above the vowel.

Gillian Aitken

Blend: | st |

Choose the correct short vowel to complete the words below.

n__st   d__st   t__st   c__st   v__st

tr__st   ch__st   l__st   f__st   cr__st

r__st   fr__st   j__st   m__st   w__st

**Write down THREE pairs of rhyming words
from the above exercise in the boxes below.**

_____	_____	_____
_____	_____	_____

Read the words below. What sound is made by the vowel sound?

cast   past   mast
vast   fast   last

Now use each word to fill in the blanks in the sentences below.

1   The ship's sail was ripped from the _____ in the
strong wind.

2   A horse has long legs and can run very _____.

3   The boy _____ his fishing-line into the river.

4   How long will this lesson _____?

5   The bus went _____ the bus-stop and did
not stop.

6   The hotel was so _____ that it had more than
a hundred bedrooms.

Blend: st

Choose the correct beginning to complete each word.

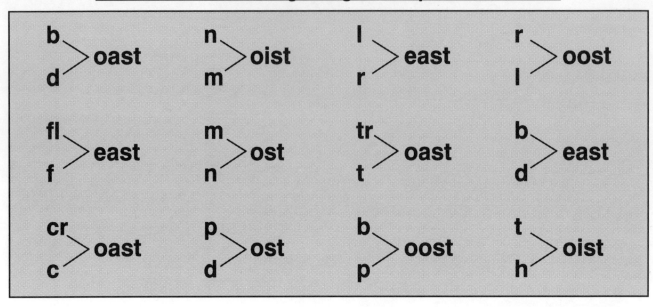

In each of the boxes below, complete the word with your answer from line one in the exercise above. Then below each word write all the other words in the same exercise which rhyme with the word in each box.

__oast	__oist	__east	__oost
_____	_____	_____	_____
_____		_____	
_____			
_____			

Now use some of the words you have found to complete the sentences.

1   The greedy boy ate ten pieces of _____ for breakfast.

2   A microphone is used to _____ the sound of a person's voice.

3   Nessie is a strange _____ which has been seen in Loch Ness in Scotland.

4   The flag was _____ed to the top of the flag pole.

5   The wedding _____ and party lasted for at _____ ten hours.

6   The girl _____ed that she would win the race, but in fact she came last.

Blend: st

Join the suffix to the base word in the word-sums below.

1 test + ed = _____	7 rest + ful = _____
2 rust + y = _____	8 crust + y = _____
3 consist + s = _____	9 dust + ing = _____
4 insist + ed = _____	10 disgust + ing = _____
5 frost + y = _____	11 mist + y = _____
6 nest + ing = _____	12 cost + ly = _____

Now use each word with suffix to complete the sentences below.

1 We had a tasty lunch of home-made soup with _____ bread.

2 In winter it is often cold and _____, but on milder days it can be damp and _____.

3 Have you seen the pair of blackbirds _____ in my back garden?

4 In our class we are _____ on our times tables every week.

5 The housekeeper did light housework such as cleaning, hoovering, _____ and polishing every week.

6 A package holiday is not very _____, and two weeks of lying in the sun is very _____.

7 The campers had left the camp site in a _____ mess with a pile of _____ tin cans and other rubbish.

8 A football team _____ of eleven people.

9 The teacher _____ on silence while the pupils did their Maths test.

Blend: st

Read the words below. Circle all the (st) blends.
(Be careful! Not all the words have an 'st' blend.)

list	must	bats	nets	lost
crust	hits	fists	rats	trust
past	sits	tests	chest	blots
cuts	just	crest	jots	dust
vests	mats	slots	frost	best

Read the sentences below, but be careful! In each sentence there are TWO words which look very similar.

1   I have lost lots of money at the races.

2   My fist fits into the glove.

3   The table juts out just a bit.

4   How much do these cots cost?

5   Do you think that vets wear vests in winter?

6   I think that some pets are pests.

Blend: st

<u>Blend each prefix with the second syllable ending in (st).</u>
<u>You should be able to make EIGHT words.</u>

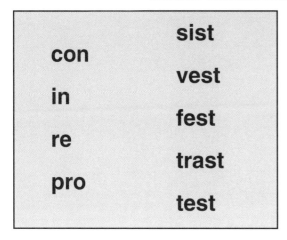

con	sist
in	vest
re	fest
pro	trast
	test

con_____   in_____

con_____   in_____

con_____   re_____

in_____   pro_____

<u>Now use each word in the sentences below.</u>

1   Sally won the swimming _____.

2   My father _____ed on giving me a lift to the station.

3   The bright sunshine in the street was a _____ to the shady garden.

4   The barn was _____ed with field mice and other rodents.

5   The drunk man _____ed arrest.

6   My family _____s of four people.

7   Many people _____ed about the building of the new road.

8   There are many ways to _____ money.

<u>Join the syllables below to make FIVE words.</u>
<u>Then match each word to the correct meaning as in the example.</u>

ex	bust _____	to join the army.
ro	sist _____	to set right, regulate.
en	just _____	to be, to live.
dis	list _____	strong, sturdy.
as	ist _exist_	to help.
ad	gust _____	a strong feeling of dislike.

Blend: sk

**Find a word ending in (sk) hidden in each line of letters
which can be used in the sentence below.**

1 a b t i s k m o p h w h i s k w
She used an electric _____ to beat the eggs.

2 b e r u s k d e s k a t u s k l
A male elephant has two ivory _____s.

3 s k i d u s k i m o b u s k y e
The time of day when it begins to get dark is called _____.

4 e t a k s v t a s k j h l i s k
A _____ is a job or duty which needs to be done.

5 m u s k o t m a k s w m a s k j
The robber's face was hidden because he wore a _____.

6 c r i s k o f d i s k a r i k s
Racing-car drivers take the _____ of having a bad accident.

7 b i r s k i s k a u b r i s k e
My grandfather likes to take a _____ walk before breakfast.

8 c q b a s k e f d a s k h u s k
The beach was full of people _____ing in the sun.

**Read the words below which have (sk) in the middle.
Then match each one to the meanings given below.**

basket   casket   musket   brisket

1 A type of gun. _____
2 A small box for valuable things. _____
3 A joint of meat. _____
4 A container made of cane for carrying things. _____

14

Blends: | sk | | sp |

Complete each word with the correct end blend (sk) or (sp).

ga___	ma___	bri___	li___	hu___
wi___	tu___	cla___	fri___	whi___
cri___	di___	ba___	gra___	de___
wa___	ta___	ra___berry		ba___et

Now write each word in the correct list.

sk

_____ _____
_____ _____
_____ _____
_____ _____
_____ _____
_____

sp

_____ _____
_____ _____
_____ _____
_____ _____

QUIZ

Look at the (sk) words. Which one means:

1   Used to store data on the computer? _____

2   To jump and run about playfully? _____

3   The dry, outer covering of grain such as
    rice or wheat? _____

Now look at the (sp) words. Which one means:

1   A stinging insect? _____

2   To hold tightly? (Two words.) _____

    _____

3   A small bundle, bunch or twist (e.g. of hair)? _____

Blends: | st | | sk |

Each word below ends with (st) or (sk).
Choose the correct blend to complete each word.

ta___	li___	mu___	ri___
be___	whi___	la___	tu___
de___	lo___	te___	di___

Write each word in the correct list below.

st   **sk**

_____ _____   _____ _____

_____ _____   _____ _____

_____ _____   _____ _____

Now choose a word ending in (st) or (sk) from the above lists
to finish each sentence. You do not have to use all the words.

1   You beat the eggs with a _____.

2   How long will the Maths _____ _____?

3   The teacher told the children to put their chairs on their
    _____s.

4   We _____ make a shopping _____ before we
    go to the shops.

5   Do you know what animal has _____s?

6   I have _____ my _____ Parker Pen.
    Have you seen it?

16

Blends: | st | | sk | | sp |

**Join the beginning of each word with the correct
end blend. Then write out each word.**

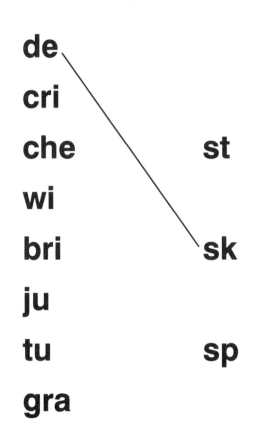

de
cri
che   st
wi
bri   sk
ju
tu   sp
gra
tru

1 _____ *desk* _____
2 _____
3 _____
4 _____
5 _____
6 _____
7 _____
8 _____
9 _____

**Complete the words below by
choosing a suitable VOWEL.**

b__sk	g__sp	f__st	l__st
w__sp	wh__sper	l__sp	d__st
j__st	br__sk	t__sk	c__st
b__sket	r__spberry	p__st	

Blends: st sk sp

Colour the balloons.

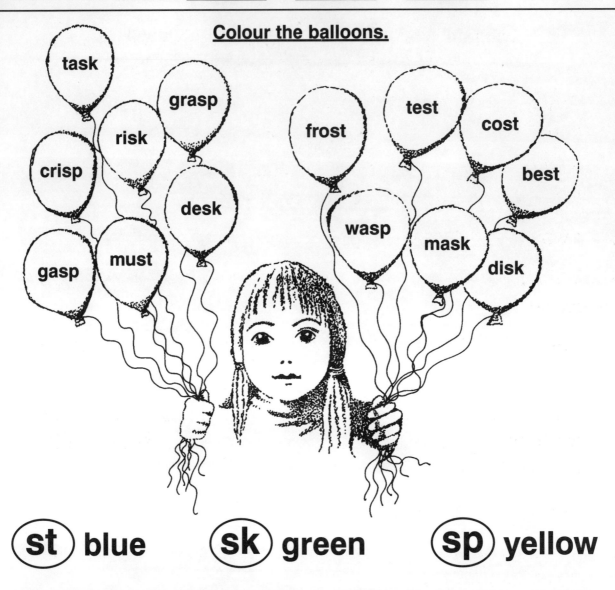

st blue   sk green   sp yellow

Now complete the sentences below using words from the balloons.

(You do NOT need to use all the words.)

1 The children wore _____s in the school play.

2 Children _____ sit at _____s in the classroom.

3 Colin gave a _____ of pain when the _____ stung him on the hand.

4 Jane got the _____ mark in the spelling _____.

5 What is the _____ of a packet of _____s?

Blends: | st | | sk | | sp |

Choose (st) (sk) or (sp) to complete the words
in the sentences below.

1 At du__ we spotted a walrus with huge tu__s ba__ing on
   some rocks ju__ a few feet away from us.

2 If people insi__ on going walking in the hills in thick mi__,
   they take the ri__ of getting lo__ .

3 I was given the ta__ of beating the eggs with a whi__ .

4 We all gave a ga__ of delight when we saw three eggs
   in the ne__ .

5 The little girl was cla__ing a small ba__et which was full
   of fresh ra__berries picked from the garden.

6 The drunk man resi__ed arre__ by struggling and shaking
   clenched fi__s at the policemen who were trying to put
   handcuffs on his wri__s.

7 The wa__ landed on Peter's de__ .

8 If you go for a bri__ walk, it means you mu__ be walking
   quite fa__ .

Now write out each word beginning with (st) (sk) or (sp)
in the correct list below.

st		sk		sp
_____ _____		_____ _____		_____
_____ _____		_____ _____		_____
_____ _____		_____ _____		_____
_____ _____		_____ _____		_____
_____ _____				

Blends: | st | | sk | | sp |

**In each line of letters find ONE word
which rhymes with the word inside the box.**

| must | j u t s j u s t u s t c u r s t |

| mask | s k i d e s k m a s t i t a s k |

| mast | s t o p a s t p a t s p o s t q |

| clasp | h w a s p g r a s p l a s t o p |

| dusk | f d u s t u k s a t u s k w e j |

| chest | i n v e t s v e s t b e t s i p |

| crisp | p i p s w i s p h a s p c i s p |

| frisk | a d i k s a b r i s k i s k y q |

| list | b i t v i s t f i t s u m i s t |

| casket | e l b a s k e t v o m u s k e t |

**Now read the words below. For each one, find
words from the above exercise which rhyme with it.**

last   husk   wrist   bask
lisp   disk   best

Blend: mp

Read the words below. Tick the ones which are REAL words.
Put a cross by the words which are NOT real words.

plump	blimp	slamp	jump
cramp	lump	rimp	stimp
lamp	shump	clamp	grump
spamp	clump	tramp	drimp

Find words ending in **in the word-square below to match the meanings.** *(Words go ACROSS or DOWN only.)*

s	b	o	d	a	m	p
t	n	s	t	a	m	p
u	t	e	h	r	l	p
m	h	u	m	p	i	g
p	u	i	d	u	m	p
c	m	k	f	s	p	t
j	p	u	m	p	u	w

1 Used to put air in tyres. _ _ _ _

2 What is left if a tree has been cut down. _ _ _ _ _

3 If you have hurt your leg, you will do this. _ _ _ _

4 You put this on a letter. _ _ _ _ _

5 A little bit wet. _ _ _ _

6 To hit somebody hard. _ _ _ _

7 You will see this on a camel's back. _ _ _ _

8 A place where rubbish is left. _ _ _ _

Blend: | mp |

Find a word ending in to match the given meanings.
The word you are looking for will rhyme with the word on the right.

?   **RHYMING WORD**

#		Meaning	Rhyme
1		slightly wet	**LAMP**
2		found on a camel's back	**JUMP**
3		type of monkey	**LIMP**
4		a homeless person	**LAMP**
5		a group or cluster (for example of trees)	**JUMP**
6		to sleep in a tent	**LAMP**
7		a small prawn	**LIMP**
8		to hit hard	**JUMP**
9		a swelling	**JUMP**
10		this might be put on a car if parked in the wrong place!	**LAMP**
11		a place where rubbish is left	**JUMP**
12		a sloping way from one level to another (for example, cars often go up one to enter a ferry)	**LAMP**

Now write the rhyming words below on the correct line.

RHYMING WORDS

LAMP: _____ _____ _____ _____ _____

JUMP: _____ _____ _____ _____ _____

LIMP: _____ _____

Blend: nd

Read the words below. Tick the ones which are REAL words.
Put a cross by the ones which are NOT real words.

hand	glend	sond	wind
grand	spand	mend	fand
flend	lend	bend	prand
pond	spend	tand	grund

Read the words below. Then use each one to fill in the
blanks in the sentences below.

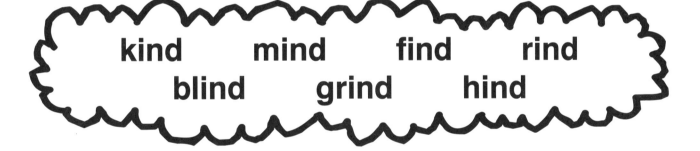

kind   mind   find   rind
blind   grind   hind

1   I can't _____ my bag. Have you seen it?

2   My dog likes eating bacon _____.

3   You have to _____ coffee beans to make coffee.

4   The _____ legs of an animal are its back legs.

5   Do you _____ if I open the window? It's very
stuffy in here.

6   The _____ man helped the _____ lady to cross
the road.

Blend: nd

**Make a real word by choosing the
correct beginning for each word below ending in** .

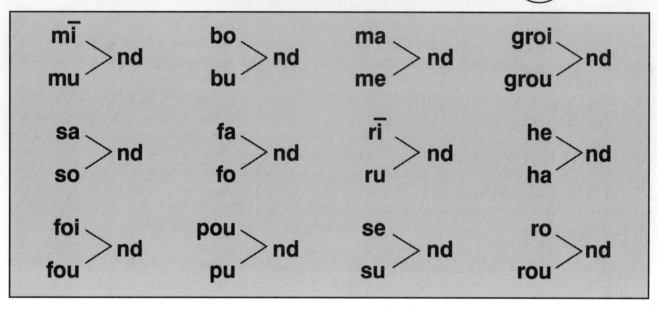

Write the 12 words you have made on the lines below.

_____   _____   _____   _____

_____   _____   _____   _____

_____   _____   _____   _____

Now use each of the above words to complete the sentences.

(The two missing words in each sentence will rhyme.)

1   I _____ a gold ring on the waste _____ near my home.

2   I must _____ for the plumber to _____ the broken pipe.

3   I don't _____ eating the bacon _____!

4   The man touched the wet _____ with his left _____.

5   The _____ between a mother and her child shows that
     they are very _____ of each other.

6   The shape of a _____ coin is _____.

24

Blend: nt

Circle the SIX nonsense words. Then put them in the bin.

bent	fant	ant	blunt
hant	spent	mint	clint
plant	munt	hunt	brant
tent	went	print	stant

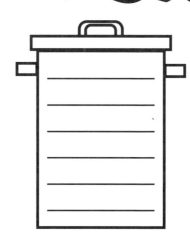

Choose the correct word to finish each sentence.

1 Tom | **spent** / **sent** | his pocket money on comics.

2 My pencil is | **blunt** / **brunt** | .

3 I | **wont** / **want** | to buy some polo | **mints** / **ments** | .

4 Ted | **bent** / **bant** | down to look at the | **ant** / **unt** | nest.

5 Does a pig | **grant** / **grunt** | ?

6 Bill | **want** / **went** | into his | **tent** / **tint** | to get his torch.

Blend: | nt |

Choose the correct short vowel to
complete each word below.

b___nt	w___nt	s___nt	h___nt
sp___nt	gr___nt	pr___nt	bl___nt
t___nt	gl___nt	spl___nt	___nt
inv___nt	spr___nt	p___nt	d___nt

Find a word ending in (nt) hidden in each line of letters
to complete each sentence below.

1 o b e q a n t v o t e n t i n t
The _____ fell down in the strong wind.

2 d i n t p l a n t b u n t a n t
Jane gave her mother a _____ as a present.

3 w e f o r n t f r o n t n t u h
The _____ of the house was painted pink.

4 a f i l n t j n n t f l i n t x
_____ is a very hard stone.

5 a n t e n t p r i n t p e n t k
The _____ was so small that I could hardly read it.

6 b e n t w a n t w o n t i n t c
What do you _____ to do tonight?

Blends: $\boxed{\text{nd}}$ $\boxed{\text{nt}}$

Shoot the balls into the correct net to score a goal.
One ball can go into BOTH nets. You score two goals for this word.

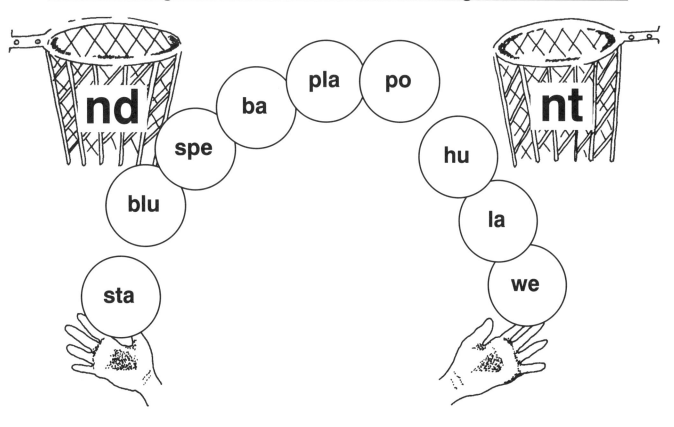

Write the words you have found on the lines below.

_____   _____   _____

_____   _____   _____

_____   _____   _____

_____

Now choose FOUR of the above words and
use them in sentences of your own.

_____

_____

_____

_____

_____

_____

_____

Blends: nd | nt

Choose (nd) or (nt) to complete the words in the sentences below.
Then write all the 'nd' or 'nt' words in the correct list.

1 The car had a de___ in its side.

2 We saw the gli___ of gold in the man's ha___.

3 Do you know who inve___ed the radio?

4 Please pri___ your name here.

5 The te___ pin is be___.

6 Can you see the a___s on the sa___?

7 In our P.E. Lesson we had to be___ down and then sta___ up ten times.

8 I always wear ti___ed glasses in the sun.

9 We spe___ a fantastic weekend at the Gra___ Hotel.

10 The man's hat blew off in the strong wi___ and la___ed in the village po___.

11 When Sally cou___ed the money in her purse, she fou___ that she had ten pou___s.

(nd) words   (nt) words

___ ___   ___ ___

___ ___   ___ ___

___ ___   ___ ___

___ ___   ___ ___

___ ___   ___ ___

Rhyming Words: | nd | | nt |

**In each line of letters find ONE word which rhymes
with the word inside the box.**

| land | m a n d a n d e n d b a n d a d |

| flint | u l p r i n t i n b l i n t e x |

| bond | f o n p o n d o n d f u n d a b |

| went | l e n d w a n t e t e n t a n t |

| mend | r e d e n d e n b e n d r i n d |

| chant | w a c h a t p l a n t e n t a n |

| kind | c a f i n d l i n d i n d i d u |

| bound | r u n d f u o n d g r o u n d k |

| paint | b e f i n t a f a i n t m i n t |

| joint | e c o i n p o i n t m o u n t h |

Write the rhyming pairs on the lines below.

_____   _____   _____   _____   _____

_____   _____   _____   _____   _____

_____   _____   _____   _____   _____

_____   _____   _____   _____   _____

Blends: nd nt

When you add (ed) suffix to words ending in (nd) and (nt),
you add another syllable. Add (ed) suffix to the words below.

(nd) words   (nt) words

end + ed = _____   print + ed = _____

hand + ed = _____   glint + ed = _____

land + ed = _____   plant + ed = _____

mend + ed = _____   sprint + ed = _____

intend + ed = _____   chant + ed = _____

**Now use each word with 'ed' suffix to fill in
the blanks in the sentences below.**

1   The young trees were _____ in spring.

2   The football fans _____ and sang before the
    match began.

3   The gold ring _____ on the woman's finger.

4   The plumber _____ the broken pipe.

5   The plane _____ safely.

6   The film _____ at midnight.

7   There was loud cheering as the runners _____ past
    the finishing line.

8   Jane _____ to go to London last weekend, but then
    changed her mind.

9   The postman _____ me a large brown envelope with
    my name _____ in big, black letters.

Blend: nd

Blend each prefix with the correct second syllable ending in (nd).
Then write each word on the lines below.

pre	pand
at	tend
in	fend
de	pend
ex	

pre_____   ex_____

at_____   ex_____

in_____   ex_____

de_____

de_____

**Now use some of the words you have made to complete
the sentences below.**

1   Whether I _____ the party or not _____s
on what time I get back from London.

2   If you _____ energy, you use it up.

3   In our drama lesson, we had to _____ to _____
ourselves from attack.

4   The Romans _____ed their empire to include
Great Britain.

**Now write your own sentences for the
two words which are left.**

_____

_____

_____

_____

Blend: | nt |

Blend each prefix with the correct second syllable ending in (nt).
Then write each word on the lines below.

con	vent
in	pent
pre	tent
ex	sent

con_____   pre_____

con_____   pre_____

con_____   ex_____

in_____

in_____

Now use some of the words you have made to complete
the sentences below.

1   Linda's parents did not give their _____ for her to stay
      at the Disco until midnight.

2   The vandals were _____ on doing as much damage
      as possible.

3   The winner of the swimming contest was _____ed
      with a gold medal.

4   From the roof top we could see the full _____ of the city.

5   It is very hard to _____ an epidemic from spreading.

Now write your own sentences for the
three words which are left.

_____

_____

_____

_____

_____

-ump   -unt

Choose the correct ending to complete the words below. Then find each word ending in (-ump) and (-unt) in the word-square below.

(Words go ACROSS and DOWN only.)

1 Sue had a big l_____ on her head where she had b_____ed it.

2 A bicycle p_____ puts air into tyres.

3 A lion is an animal which h_____s.

4 If your pencil is bl_____, you should sharpen it.

5 How many h_____s has a camel got?

6 A st_____ man can do many fantastic things like j_____ing off roofs.

7 A pig makes a gr_____ing noise.

8 R_____ steak is very expensive.

9 A pl_____ person is not thin.

10 The men cut down the tall tree, leaving only a st_____.

11 The man was sl_____ed in a chair, sound asleep.

x	a	l	u	m	p	b	s	f
b	s	v	b	c	i	l	c	y
u	t	a	h	g	r	u	n	t
m	u	s	r	h	u	n	t	s
p	m	t	w	e	k	t	y	l
g	p	u	m	p	z	x	j	u
d	e	n	r	u	m	p	u	m
t	l	t	f	p	l	u	m	p
m	v	r	k	h	u	m	p	o

Blends: $\boxed{\text{nd}}$ $\boxed{\text{nt}}$ $\boxed{\text{mp}}$

Join the beginning of each word with the correct ending.
Then write each word on the lines provided.

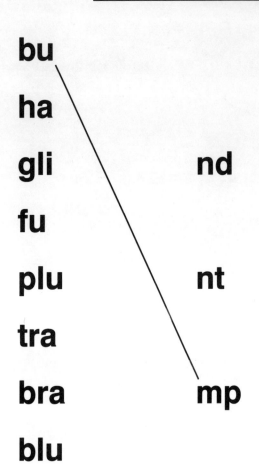

bu

ha

gli   nd

fu

plu   nt

tra

bra   mp

blu

spri

1 *bump*

2 _____

3 _____

4 _____

5 _____

6 _____

7 _____

8 _____

9 _____

Choose the TWO correct endings which can complete each word:
$\textcircled{\text{nd}}$ $\textcircled{\text{nt}}$ or $\textcircled{\text{mp}}$.

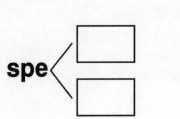

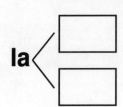

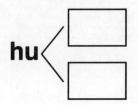

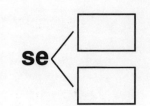

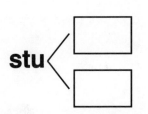

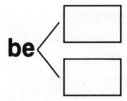

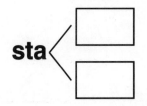

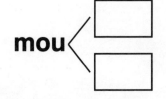

Blends: | nd | | nt | | mp |

Colour the balloons.

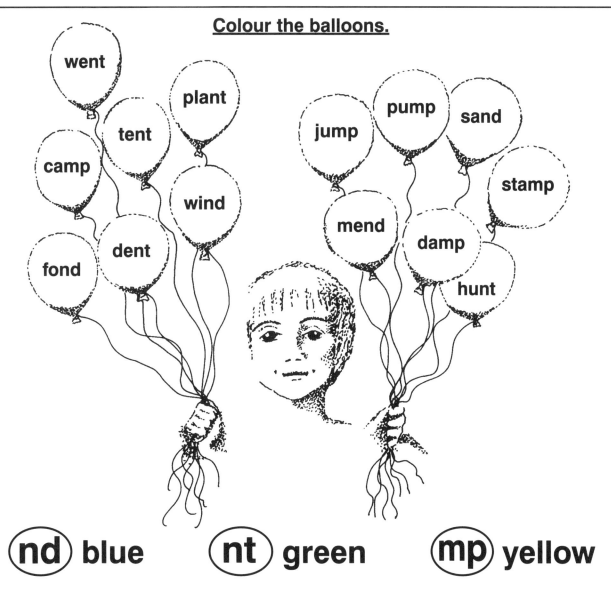

nd blue   **nt** green   **mp** yellow

Now complete the sentences below using words from the balloons.
You do not need to use all the words.

1   I am very _____ of my little cat.

2   The strong _____ blew down some of the _____s
    in the _____ site.

3   After the crash, the car was badly _____ed.

4   Sally found a 1st class _____ in the _____ pit.

5   Tim _____ed the puncture, _____ed up the
    tyres and then _____ for a ride.

Blend: ng

Circle the SIX nonsense words. Then put them in the bin.

bang	stang	swing	lung
clong	sling	song	thing
king	lang	wing	tring
dang	rung	cling	spung

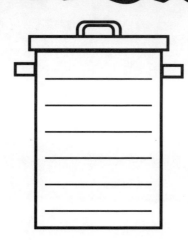

Choose the correct word to finish each sentence.

1 Please [**bring** / **ring**] me your book.

2 The bee [**sting** / **stung**] him on the hand.

3 Rachel fell off the [**wing** / **swing**], and now her arm is in a [**sling** / **sing**].

4 In [**spring** / **sprung**] we can hear the birds [**sting** / **sing**].

5 I am going to [**hung** / **hang**] up the washing on the line.

Blend: ng

Choose the correct short vowel to complete the words below.

th__ng	br__ng	k__ng
spr__ng	sw__ng	b__ng
r__ng	s__ng	g__ng	h__ng
sl__ng	p__ng-p__ng	l__ng

Now find a word ending in (ng) hidden in the line of letters to complete the sentences below.

1 **w a s t r i n g r i n g p a n g**

You must tie up the parcel with _____.

2 **s i n g l o n g a h e c l u n g**

The child _____ to his mother's hand when crossing the road.

3 **b t s p u n g a n g w f r u n g**

The last _____ of the ladder was broken.

4 **a y f i l n g f l u n g o j h r**

The boy _____ the twig into the river.

5 **b d o n g b a n g r i m d i n g k**

There was a loud _____ when the bomb went off.

Blend: ng

Add suffix (ing) to the words below:

long + ing = _____   sling + ing = _____

bang + ing = _____   cling + ing = _____

sting + ing = _____   bring + ing = _____

hang + ing = _____   swing + ing = _____

Now use each word + (ing) to fill in the blanks in the sentences below.

1   The baby monkey was _____ to its mother.

2   The clothes were _____ on the washing line.

3   A wasp is a _____ insect.

4   I am _____ for the summer holidays to begin.

5   After _____ his school bag over his shoulder, Tom set off for school.

6   I was woken up by a loud _____ noise from the house next door.

7   The boys were told off for _____ on the gate.

8   The postman arrived at 8 o'clock, _____ a pile of letters.

Now add (ing) to the words below and use the word + suffix in sentences of your own.

ring + ing = _____   sing + ing = _____

_____

_____

_____

_____

Blend: nk

Make a real word by choosing the correct ending.

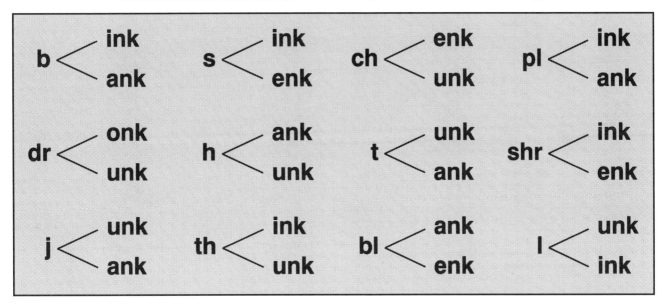

Now write the words you have made in the correct list below.

(-ank) words	(-ink) words	(-unk) words
_____	_____	_____
_____	_____	_____
_____	_____	_____
_____	_____	_____

(nk) QUIZ

Find the (nk) word to match the meanings given below.

1 An animal which has beautiful fur. _ _ _ _

2 An animal which can give off a very bad smell. _ _ _ _ _

3 A place where you go ice-skating. _ _ _ _

4 A bed which is above or below another one. _ _ _ _

5 A colour. _ _ _ _

6 To close and open both eyes very quickly,
   for example when you look at a bright light. _ _ _ _ _

7 To go below the surface of water. _ _ _ _

8 To smell very badly. _ _ _ _ _

Blend: nk

Choose a short vowel to complete the words below.

bl__nk	t__nk	shr__nk	h__nk
b__nk	dr__nk	st__nk	th__nk
r__nk	p__nk	pl__nk	sk__nk
j__nk	cr__nk	sp__nk	l__nk

Read the words below. Then use each one to fill in the blanks in the sentences.

shrink   chink   drank   stink   blank
junk   skunk   honk   blink   thank

1 Looking at the bright light made him _____.

2 We could see daylight through a _____ in the curtains.

3 A _____ is an animal which gives off a terrible _____ to defend itself.

4 If somebody gives you a present, you should _____ them.

5 We could hear the _____ing of the fog horn from the coast.

6 I had a dream that I _____ some magic medicine which made me _____ to the size of a doll.

7 The attic was full of all kinds of _____.

8 We were told to write our names on a _____ piece of paper.

Blends: ng nk

Find 10 words ending in ng or nk in the word-square to match the pictures. Write each word below the picture.

(Words go ACROSS or DOWN only.)

_____ _____ _____

_____

w	i	n	k	a	h	g	a	o
i	d	x	s	i	n	k	n	j
y	s	t	i	n	g	t	f	s
j	b	c	b	f	e	h	m	i
r	a	k	i	n	g	i	u	n
i	n	t	e	d	l	n	v	g
n	k	a	k	p	c	k	t	i
g	w	n	q	h	k	s	g	l
x	n	k	r	s	l	i	n	g

_____

_____

_____

Now write the words you have found on the lines below in ALPHABETICAL order.

1 _____   6 _____
2 _____   7 _____
3 _____   8 _____
4 _____   9 _____
5 _____   10 _____

Blends: ng nk

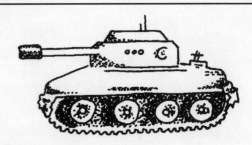

EXERCISE 1 – Listen to the words read to you.
They all end in (ng) or (nk). Write the words on the lines below.

1 _____   6 _____

2 _____   7 _____

3 _____   8 _____

4 _____   9 _____

5 _____   10 _____

EXERCISE 2 – Read the sentences below. Circle the correct word.

1 Don't | **brink** / **bring** | that smelly | **thing** / **think** | inside.

2 The bird has broken its | **wing** / **wink** | .

3 What do you | **thing** / **think** | of my gold | **ring** / **rink** | ?

4 The bee has just | **stung** / **stunk** | him on the head.

5 He went into the | **bang** / **bank** | to get some money.

6 He | **hung** / **hunk** | his hat on the peg.

7 The ship | **sang** / **sank** | in five minutes.

Blends: ng nk

Shoot the balls into the correct net to score a goal.
One ball can go into BOTH nets. You score two goals for this word.

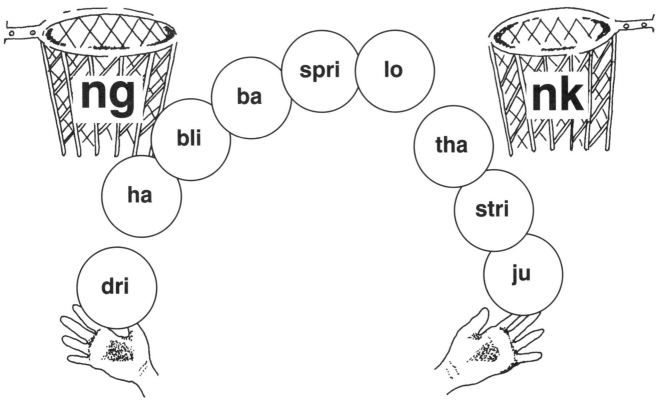

Write the words you have found on the lines below.

_____   _____   _____

_____   _____   _____

_____   _____   _____

_____

Now choose FOUR of the above words and use them
in sentences of your own.

_____

_____

_____

_____

_____

_____

Blends: |ng| |nk|

**Choose the correct blend to finish each word
in the sentences below.**

1   Not all insects have wi___s.

2   The dru___ man was si___ing a so___ to himself.

3   The si___ was full of dirty dishes.

4   The baby monkey was cli___ing to its mother.

5   She tied up the parcel with stri___.

6   When Tom tried to hit the wasp, it stu___ him on
    the hand.

7   The children slept on bu___ beds in the caravan.

8   Another name for the table-tennis is pi___- po___.

9   The bridesmaids were wearing lo___, pi___ dresses.

10 The steps on a ladder are called ru___s.

11 A sku___ is a small animal which can make
    a terrible sti___!

12 When they heard the go___, they went into dinner.

13 The ga___way to the ship was just a narrow pla___.

14 When Bill flu___ the rock into the river, it quickly
    sa___ to the bottom.

-ing   -ink

**Choose (-ing) or (-ink) to complete the words
in the sentences below.**

1   Don't br____ that smelly th____ in here. It st____s.

2   A bee can st____.

3   The k____ was given a dr____ in a golden cup.

4   Jane fell off the sw____ and hurt her arm, so now it is
in a sl____.

5   The bird has a broken w____.

6   If you bl____ you shut your eyes, but if you w____ you
close just one eye.

7   In Spr____ we can hear the birds s____.

8   Do you th____ that p____ and red go well together?

**Now find each word ending in (-ing) or (-ink) from the above sentences
in the word-square.** *(Words go ACROSS or DOWN only.)*

a	b	r	i	n	g	f	u	e	w
t	h	i	n	g	m	a	d	e	j
o	f	s	l	i	n	g	r	q	d
t	s	w	p	i	n	k	i	y	s
h	i	i	s	p	r	i	n	g	t
i	n	n	b	l	i	n	k	o	i
n	g	g	x	o	y	w	p	f	n
k	i	n	g	a	h	i	o	y	g
w	i	n	g	d	z	n	e	a	z
e	c	s	t	i	n	k	l	u	j

Blends: | ng | | nk |

**Blend the Beginning, Middle and End sounds below to make
11 words ending in (ng) or (nk).**

h			
b	a	ng	
r	u	nk	
th			

h_____   b_____

h_____   r_____

h_____   r_____

b_____   r_____

b_____   th_____

b_____

**Now use some of the words to fill in the blanks
in the sentences below.**

1   If you have a cold, your nose feels _____ed up.

2   The soup was served with a large _____ of crusty bread.

3   The soldier was promoted to the _____ of captain.

4   Steps on a ladder are called _____s.

5   When the bell _____, the children went into class.

6   Philip _____ his wet socks from the end of his
    _____ bed to dry.

Now use the remaining FOUR words in sentences of your own.

_____

_____

_____

_____

_____

_____

_____

_____

Blends: ng nk

Blend the Beginning, Middle and End sounds below to make
10 words ending in (ng) or (nk).

```
r
s        o        ng
m
l        i        nk
th
```

r_____   m_____

r_____   l_____

s_____   l_____

s_____   th_____

s_____   th_____

Now use each word to fill in the blanks
in the sentences below.

1   The Duchess wore a _____ coat, and a huge diamond _____ glinted on her left hand.

2   I _____ I have lost one of my cuff _____s.

3   We spent a _____ time at the ice _____.

4   I was given the microphone and told to _____ a sad _____.

5   If some_____ is made of wood, it will not _____ if you put it in water.

Blends: ng nk

**In each line of letters find TWO words
which rhyme with the word inside the box.**

gong	w x l o n g s o n g h o n g e t
bank	i d r a n k i n g h p l a n k d
ring	h s p r i n g k i n g i n g j o
slang	f u b a n g o h a n g s l i n g
pink	c r i n k p i c k d r i n k i n
flung	a d l u n g h a r u n g u n t o
chunk	p r b u n k s k u n k t a n k h
sung	a s t u n g o n g h u n g u m g
junk	e f s h r u n k i d r u n k i p
wing	l t i n g b r i n g t h i n g l
rank	f u s a n k t h a n k c a n k g
brink	a s h i n k a b l i n k l i n k

How good is your memory?

**Cover up the exercise you have just done.
Can you think of THREE words which rhyme with:**

1 **RING** _____ _____ _____

2 **BRINK** _____ _____ _____

Blends: mp ng nk

Complete the words in the sentences below with
mp ng or nk.

1 The du___ was full of ju___ and rusty old thi___s.

2 I thi___ my weddi___ ri___ has gone down the plug hole in the kitchen si___.

3 I tha___ed the waiter for bri___ing me a dri___ of water.

4 The light from the la___ was so bright that it made us bli___.

5 We did not get a wi___ of sleep because of the ba___ing and thu___ing from the house next door.

6 The pet chi___ was playing happily with a bit of stri___.

7 You can't buy sta___s from a ba___.

8 When she washed her pi___, woollen ju___er in hot water, it shra___.

9 The mattress on the top bu___ bed was very hard as it had no spri___s.

10 When the sun at last sa___ behind the hills, the sky remained pi___ and red for a long time.

11 A big lu___ came up on Pam's arm where the bee had stu___ her.

12 The ca___ers hu___ their da___ clothes from the washing-line tied to tent poles.

Blend: nch

Put in the correct short vowel to complete the words below.
(More than one short vowel can be used in a few words.)

b___nch	Fr___nch	cr___nch	p___nch
st___nch	br___nch	cl___nch	h___nch
tr___nch	wr___nch	l___nch	m___nch
dr___nch	w___nch	fl___nch	qu___nch

Now add suffixes to the (nch) words below.

1 clench + ed = _____   6 punch + ing = _____

2 lunch + es = _____   7 branch + es = _____

3 bunch + es = _____   8 bench + es = _____

4 trench + es = _____   9 drench + ed = _____

5 launch + ed = _____   10 winch + ed = _____

Now use each word + suffix to fill in the blanks in the sentences below.

1 _____ of ripe bananas hung from the _____ of the trees.

2 The boy _____ his fists, and began _____ the child who had attacked him.

3 The park _____ were full of people eating picnic _____.

4 The helicopter _____ the man to safety.

5 The lifeboat was _____ in only two minutes.

6 The men fighting in the _____ got _____ by the heavy rain.

Blend: nge

<u>Complete the (nge) words below by choosing the correct vowel.</u>

ch__nge	t__nge	l__nge	s__nge
rev__nge	h__nge	arr__nge	b__nge
cr__nge	wh__nge	fr__nge	r__nge
tw__nge	str__nge	gr__nge	pl__nge

<u>Find TWO words from the above exercise to which you can add suffix (er) to match the meanings given below.</u>

(Note: As 'er' is a vowel suffix, you must drop the 'e' of the base word.)

1   Somebody who is not known to you   _____

2   A person in charge of a game park or forest   _____

<u>The meanings of two (nge) words are given below.
What two vowels must you add to complete each word?</u>

l___nge   =   sitting-room, to laze about.

scr___nge   =   to cadge, get money (or other things) by begging.

<u>The meanings of three more words are given below.
What letter must you add to complete each word?</u>

ding____   =   dark, dreary, dull.

sting____   =   mean, not generous.

spong____   =   light, porous, absorbent.

<u>The meanings of three more words are given below.
This time, what TWO letters are needed to complete each word?</u>

ging____   =   a root plant used to flavour food.

dang____   =   situation of threat, peril.

mang____   =   long, open box or trough for horses or cattle
                 to feed in.

Blend: nce

Find words to rhyme with the word in the box to match the meanings given below.

RHYMING WORD: **DANCE**

1 A country in Europe. ____________
2 To look quickly at something. ____________
3 Sleep-like condition (for example to be hypnotised). ____________
4 To increase the value of attraction of something. En____________
5 Fortune, luck, possibility. ____________
6 Position, pose, point of view. ____________
7 (Of a horse) To move by lifting the front legs high, and springing from the back legs. ____________
8 Weapon with long shaft and pointed steel head. ____________

RHYMING WORD: **DISTANCE**

1 Way in. ____________
2 Example. ____________
3 To weigh; equalise two sides of something. ____________

RHYMING WORD: **SINCE**

1 Son of a king. ____________
2 To chop meat into small pieces. ____________
3 To flinch or draw back (for example in pain). ____________
4 To make somebody believe something. Con____________

RHYMING WORD: **FLOUNCE**

1 A unit of weight (one sixteenth of a pound). ____________
2 To proclaim, make known to the public. An____________
3 To swoop. ____________
4 To spring back after hitting the ground (for example, ball). ____________

Ending: ance

Words ending in ance are NOUNS. Very often there is
a related VERB or ADJECTIVE.

For example:	NOUNS
annoy (verb)	annoyance
reluctant (adjective)	reluctance

Change the following VERBS into NOUNS by adding ance.

(Remember your suffixing rules.)

VERB	NOUN with 'ance'	VERB	NOUN with 'ance'
perform	_____	defy	_____
disturb	_____	ally	_____
appear	_____	resist	_____
attend	_____	grieve	_____
insure	_____	annoy	_____

**Now change the following ADJECTIVES into NOUNS by
changing ant to ance.**

ADJECTIVE	NOUN
important	_____
repugnant	_____
tolerant	_____
arrogant	_____
ignorant	_____
distant	_____

**Use some of the 'ance' words from the above exercises in sentences
of your own. Try and use more than one in each sentence.**

E.g. There was a **disturbance** outside the hall during the
performance.

Ending: ence

Words ending in (ence) are <u>NOUNS</u>. Very often there is
a related <u>VERB</u> or <u>ADJECTIVE</u>.

For example:	**NOUNS**
refer (verb)	**refer<u>ence</u>**
negligent (adjective)	**neglig<u>ence</u>**

Change the following VERBS into NOUNS by adding (ence).

VERB	NOUN with 'ence'	VERB	NOUN with 'ence'
interfere	_____	exist	_____
persevere	_____	depend	_____
coincide	_____	prefer	_____
correspond	_____	excel	_____

Now change the following ADJECTIVES into NOUNS in the same way.

ADJECTIVE	NOUN	ADJECTIVE	NOUN
different	_____	confident	_____
present	_____	patient	_____
insolent	_____	absent	_____
indolent	_____	permanent	_____
competent	_____	evident	_____

VOCABULARY QUIZ: Choose (ence) words from the above exercise.

1 Which **TWO** words are opposite in meaning? _____ _____

2 Which **THREE** words describe positive
personal qualities?   _____ _____ _____

3 Which **TWO** words describe negative
personal qualities?   _____ _____

4 Which word describes a state lasting indefinitely?   _____

5 Which word means proof?   _____

6 Which word means lack of interest or concern when you add
the prefix 'in' to the beginning of the word?   _____

Blends: | nch | nge | nce |

Join the beginning of each word with the correct ending.
Then write each word on the lines provided.

plu	
be	
da	**nch**
pri	
Fre	**nge**
mi	
pu	**nce**
fri	
fe	

1 _____

2 _____

3 _____

4 _____

5 _____

6 _____

7 _____

8 _____

9 _____

Now complete the words in the sentences below with the
correct end blend: (nch) (nge) or (nce).

1   If you go to Fra___ you will have a good cha___ to speak
    a lot of Fre___ !

2   The man lu___d at his attacker in self-defe___.

3   The handsome pri___ da___d with Cinderella at the Ball.

4   I was convi___d that I had been given the wrong cha___
    when I bought a can of Coke to que___ my thirst.

5   At first gla___ the man on the park be___ in the dista___
    looked like my father, but in fact he was a stra___r.

6   At the party, we had to bala___ a bu___ of bananas on our
    heads, and bou___ a ball at the same time!

Blend: ft

Find words in the word-square ending in **to match the meanings given below.**

(Words go ACROSS and DOWN only.)

a	d	r	i	f	t	o	h	s
n	s	h	a	f	t	c	l	w
c	h	q	l	i	f	t	r	i
r	i	e	k	g	w	q	z	f
a	f	g	d	p	l	o	f	t
f	t	i	s	d	r	a	f	t
t	u	f	t	v	i	x	m	u
b	j	t	i	g	r	a	f	t
i	e	f	t	s	o	f	t	j

1   A present.   _ _ _ _ _

2   To go without aim or purpose.   _ _ _ _ _ _

3   Opposite of hard.   _ _ _ _

4   Opposite of right.   _ _ _

5   Area below roof, often used as storage space.   _ _ _ _

6   To move something.   _ _ _ _ _

7   To raise.   _ _ _ _

8   A first or rough copy of something written.   _ _ _ _ _

9   A bunch (of hair, grass, etc) held together at the base.   _ _ _ _

10   Skill or trade involving handiwork.   _ _ _ _ _

11   Very fast.   _ _ _ _ _

12   Long narrow vertical space which a lift goes up and down.   _ _ _ _ _

13   If you have suffered a bad burn, you might need a skin   _ _ _ _ _

Endings: ┌─ **ft** ─┐ ┌─ **ff** ─┐

Fill in the blanks in the sentences below with the correct letters
(**ff**) **or** (**ft**).

1   From the top of the cli___ we could see a life-ra___
    tossing about on the waves below.

2   The dog sni___ed the white stu___ in the plastic bag,
    but one whi___ made it sneeze violently.

3   If you fall down the li___ sha___ you will kill yourself.

4   A___er he had finished the first dra___ of his essay,
    he made himself a cup of co___ee.

5   By mistake he le___ his birthday gi___ in the taxi.

6   Mrs Jones dri___ed o___ to sleep while listening to
    so___ music on the radio.

7   The scru___y looking man spoke to us in a gru___
    voice.

8   In handicra___ lessons the children learnt how to make
    small, flu___y animals.

9   The boy undid the buttons on his le___ cu___,
    because the doctor wanted to see the scar from his
    skin gra___.

10 He spent all day shi___ing piles of junk from his
    lo___ to the garden shed, and felt very st___ the next
    day as a result.

Blend: ld

Find words to rhyme with the word in the box to match the meanings given below.

RHYMING WORD:

BOLD

1 Precious metal. _____

2 Not hot. _____

3 Not young. _____

4 To have or keep something in your hand(s). _____

5 What you do with a letter before putting it in the envelope. _____

6 Exchanged for money. _____

7 Informed. _____

8 To tell off. _____

RHYMING WORD:

CHILD

1 Not tame, uncontrolled. _____

2 Gentle, not harsh or severe. _____

RHYMING WORD:

BALD

1 To burn with a hot liquid. _____

RHYMING WORD:

SHIELD

1 Enlosed area of land for crops or grazing animals. _____

Note the important words below which end in (ld).
In these words the 'l' is silent. Use each one in a sentence of your own in your exercise books.

could   would   should

Blend: lt

Read the words below which all end in lt.
Then match each one to the meanings given below.

> wilt   halt   guilt   pelt   jolt
> quilt   silt   consult   tilt

1   Thick bed covering. _____

2   Sediment of fine soil found in river beds. _____

3   To stop. _____

4   Flowers will do this if they are not watered. _____

5   To seek information or advice from somebody. _____

6   What you might feel if you have done something wrong. _____

7   Skin of a wild animal. _____

8   To shake or move with a jerk. _____

9   To take up a sloping or slanting position. _____

Find SEVEN words ending in lt in the mini word-square below.
Then use each one to fill in the blanks in the sentences.

(Words go ACROSS or DOWN only.)

1   Please pass me the _____ and pepper.

2   The Scotsman was wearing a _____.

3   The warm sun made the snow _____.

4   His exam _____ was very good.

5   The roses _____ wonderful.

6   The accident was not his _____.

7   She _____ faint in the crowded lift.

s	m	e	l	t	f
a	k	i	l	t	a
l	v	a	i	m	u
t	c	h	j	e	l
r	e	s	u	l	t
g	f	e	l	t	q

Blends: | ld | | lt |

Choose the correct ending to finish each word.

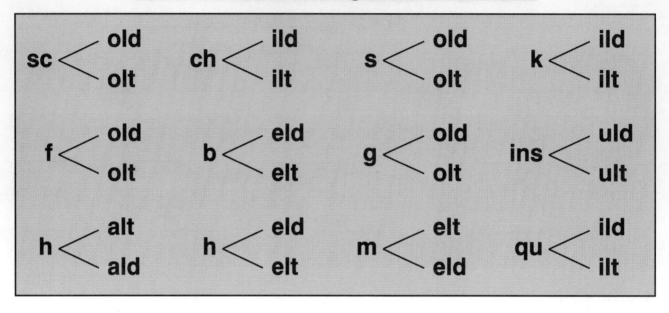

Choose the correct word so that each sentence makes sense.

1   The horse started to | **bolt** / **bold** | when it | **smeld** / **smelt** | smoke.

2   The child was | **told** / **tolt** | to | **hold** / **holt** | his sister's hand when crossing the road.

3   The girl | **speld** / **spelt** | her teacher's name wrongly.

4   The flowers will | **wild** / **wilt** | unless you water them.

5   The | **bold** / **bald** | man | **felt** / **feld** | | **cold** / **colt** | without a hat in the wind.

6   The | **colt** / **cold** | was running about the | **fielt** / **field** | with its mother.

Blends: | ld | | lt |

Choose the correct blend to complete the words in the sentences below.

1 The chi___ he___ his mother's hand as he crossed the road.

2 The Scotsman loosened the be___ of his ki___ because it fe___ too tight.

3 The boy was sco___ed because he spi___ the sa___ all over the table cloth.

4 The liquid in the glass sme___ like ma___ whisky.

5 If you sca___ yourself badly, you should consu___ a doctor.

6 The man was full of gui___ because the accident had been his fau___.

7 When the weather turned mi___ after the long, co___ spell, the snow began to me___.

8 I was to___ to lock and bo___ the door.

9 The skin of a wi___ animal is called a pe___.

10 The woman so___ her go___ earrings because she needed the money.

Now write the (ld) and (lt) words in the correct list below.

(ld) **words**	(lt) **words**
_____ _____ _____	_____ _____ _____
_____ _____ _____	_____ _____ _____
_____ _____ _____	_____ _____ _____
_____	_____ _____
	_____

Blends: | lk | lp | lb |

These blends come at the end of words or syllables.
They are used after ĭ, ŭ and ĕ.

Circle the blend in the words below.

(Be careful! Not all the words have the blend you are looking for.)

(lk)	black	milky	silken	slick	
	blink	hulk	bulk	sulky	kiln
(lp)	clap	gulp	plop	pulp	play
	people	help	yelp	plot	
(lb)	blob	blubber	bulb	plod	
	bold	sold			

Join the beginning of each word with the correct ending to make 10 words.

(One beginning can blend with two endings.)

mĭ	
gŭ	
sĭ	lk
bŭ	
hŭ	lp
hĕ	
pŭ	lb
yĕ	
sŭ	

_____   _____

_____   _____

_____   _____

_____   _____

_____

Which end blend only makes one word? _____

Which beginning can have two possible endings? _____

Blends: ld lt lk lp lf

Visual discrimination sheet

Look carefully to find the word in the box hidden in the line of letters. The number on the right tells you how many times the word is hidden in the line of letters.

felt	l e f t f e l t f e l t f l e t l	2
milk	k i m i l k m i k l m i l k l i m	2
smelt	s l e m t m e l t s m e l t e l t	1
hold	j h o l d h e l d h o l d h l o d	2
belt	b l e t e l d e l t b e l t l e b	1
self	e l f s e l f s l e f s e l f s e	2
spelt	t s p l i t e s p e l t s p l e t	1
bald	b d a l b b l a d b a l d b a l d	2
help	p h l e p e l h l h e l p h e l p	2
golf	k u g u l f g l o f g o l f o l g	1
cold	w a c o l d c o l d c l o d o l c	2
sulk	v s i l k s l u k s u l k s l i k	1
salt	o h s a l t s l a t a l s a l t q	2
sold	a s o l d s l o d s o l d s o l d	3
gulp	p l u g u l p l g u l p g l u p l	2

Blend: If

Read the words below ending in If.
Use each one to fill in the blanks in the sentences.

shelf   Gulf   golf   elf   wolf

1   My father likes to play _____ in his free time.

2   An _____ is like a little fairy.

3   Put the glasses on the top _____.

4   A _____ is a wild dog which hunts in a pack.

5   The _____ stream is the warm ocean current which flows from the _____ of Mexico. *(Use the same word for each blank.)*

SELF

> The word **SELF** is usually part of my**self**, your**self**, etc.
> For the plural we use **SELVES**.
> For example, our**selves**, them**selves,** etc.

Complete the words below with 'self' or 'selves'.

my____   your____   her____   it____   him____

our_____   your_____   them_____

Now use each of the above words to complete the sentences below.

1   The cat washed _____ all over.

2   "Behave _____," said the teacher to the naughty child.

3   The children warmed _____ by the camp fire.

4   We had to cook for _____ when we went to camp.

5   Bill hurt _____ when he fell off his bike.

6   Sally bought _____ a new pair of jeans.

7   "Help _____ to ice-cream and jelly," said Tom's mum to the children he had invited to his party.

8   After bathing, I dried _____ with a towel.

Words ending in: | If |

What is different about these words?

half   calf

Use each word in a sentence of your own.

_____

_____

_____

_____

There is a spelling change when words ending in 'If' are used in the plural.

For example: one el**f**   two el**ves**

Write the plural form of the words below.

SINGULAR	PLURAL
one shelf	a number of _____
one wolf	a pack of _____
one calf	three _____
one half	two _____
myself	_____

There are other words ending in 'f' which change to 'ves' in the plural.

Change the words below from singular to plural.

SINGULAR	PLURAL
leaf	_____
loaf	_____
knife	_____
wife	_____
life	_____
sheaf	_____

Blends: [lve] [lge]

Match the words below to the meanings.

$\{$ **delve   solve   valve** $\}$

1   Device used for controlling flow of liquid or air.   _____

2   To find an answer (to a problem).   _____

3   To dig or search into (a problem or issue).   _____

Make FIVE words from the table ending in (lve).

Then use each word to complete the sentences.

dis e re in	volve solve

_____

_____

_____

_____

_____

1   Birds have _____d from reptiles that used to live in trees.

2   The earth _____s around the sun.

3   Sugar _____s in hot water.

4   Jenny _____d to work harder after getting a bad school report.

5   Being a teacher _____s a lot of marking and report writing.

Look at the THREE words below ending in (lge). Check the meanings
in a dictionary and then use each one in a sentence of your own.

$\{$ **bulge   indulge   divulge** $\}$

_____

_____

_____

_____

Blend: ct

Blend the prefix with the second syllable ending in (ct) to make SIX words. Then use each one to fill in the blanks in the sentences.

con	rect
im	tect
di	lect
re	vict
de	spect
col	pact

_____

_____

_____

_____

_____

_____

1   The woman's speech made a big _____ on the people listening.

2   I asked a passer-by to _____ me to the station.

3   I used to _____ stamps when I was a child.

4   The spoilt child showed a marked lack of _____ to his parents and teachers.

5   The police could not _____ any sign of fingerprints.

6   A life-sentence is usually given to those _____ed of murder.

Read the words below which all begin with the prefix 'con' and end in the blend (ct). Match each one to the meanings given.

contact	conduct	concoct
conflict	contract	construct

1   Dispute, clashing of opposite sides.   _____

2   To make or build.   _____

3   To do or behave, to control an orchestra.   _____

4   To make up or invent.   _____

5   A formal, written agreement.   _____

6   To get in touch with somebody, communicate.   _____

Blend: | ct |

Blend the prefix with the second syllable ending in (ct) to make SIX words. Then use each one to fill in the blanks in the sentences.

ad	flect
re	pect
com	tact
ex	rect
in	pact
cor	dict

_____

_____

_____

_____

_____

_____

1   I did not _____ to pass my driving test first time.

2   The willow trees were _____ed in the clear water of the lake.

3   A _____ disc should last longer than a cassette.

4   The drug _____ was referred to a clinic for treatment.

5   The teacher told the child to _____ his spelling mistakes.

6   The china dog fell off the shelf, but luckily it landed _____.

Read the 'ct' words below beginning with the prefix 'in'. They are all VERBS. Use each one to fill in the blanks in the phrases below.

> inspect   inflict   instruct
> inject   infect

1   To _____ pain.

2   To _____ a learner.

3   To _____ a vaccine into somebody's vein.

4   To _____ a room for tidiness.

5   To _____ somebody with a cold.

Blend: pt

Read the one-syllable words below which all end in (pt).

leapt   kept   apt   wept   script

opt   crypt   slept

Which word means:

To choose?   _____

Something which is written?   _____

A vault below a church?   _____

Suitable, likely (to do something)?   _____

The other four words are all VERBS in the PAST tense.

For example: **slept** = past tense of the verb **SLEEP**

Fill in the correct forms for the remaining three verbs.

_____ = past tense of the verb _____

_____ = past tense of the verb _____

_____ = past tense of the verb _____

ANAGRAM:

Unscramble the letters of the word below to find a country.

P Y E T G   _____

Read the words below which all end in the same sound
as words ending in (pt).

ripped   **hopped**   **snapped**   **gripped**

Why are these words spelled differently?
Can you think of any other words which have the same pattern?
If so, write them on the lines below.

_____   _____   _____

Blend: pt

In the exercises below blend each prefix with
the correct second syllable to make FIVE words ending in **pt**.
(One prefix has to be used twice in each case.)
Then use each word to fill in the blanks in the sentences.

cor	
ac	**opt**
ad	**rupt**
inter	**cept**

_____
_____
_____
_____
_____

1   It is rude to _____ somebody while he or she is speaking.
2   The child was _____ed at the age of two.
3   The missile was _____ed before it hit its target.
4   The _____ policeman was found guilty of _____ing bribes.

ad	**cept**
dis	**rupt**
con	**apt**
e	**script**

_____
_____
_____
_____
_____

1   The badly behaved child frequently _____ed the lesson.
2   A _____ is an idea or notion.
3   The smoking volcano looked as if it was about to _____.
4   An army _____ who has just been called up might find it hard
    to _____ to army life.

Read the four words below which end in the difficult blend **mpt**.
Check the meaning of these words in a dictionary if you don't know the
meaning. Then use each one in a sentence of your own.

contempt   unkempt   exempt   attempt

TEACHING NOTES AND GUIDELINES

Worksheet 1   st

The blend 'st' is a common one, and also found at the beginning of words (see *"Spotlight on Blends", Book One,* Worksheets 1 and 2). This worksheet focuses on fairly simple words ending in 'st' with a short vowel in the middle. In the first exercise, some of the words can be completed with more than one short vowel (for example, l_st, r_st, m_st). The second exercise focuses on words ending in 'st' which have 'a' in the middle pronounced like the 'a' in 'bath'. Dyslexics often associate this sound with the 'ar' spelling choice, and might spell words in this group as 'carst', 'parst', etc. (Pupils can be reminded of the rule that 'ar' is only used when followed by a single consonant, not when followed by a consonant blend as here.) The sentence completion exercise is straightforward as only one word is omitted from each sentence, and the vocabulary level is not high.

Worksheet 2   st

The first exercise is an onset-and-rime blending exercise, but the words focused on have long sounds in the middle, or vowel diphthongs as in *'hoist'.* The instructions for the follow-up rhyming exercise might be best given orally, as it was difficult to avoid rather wordy written instructions. Teachers might like to alert pupils to the fact that most rhyming words will not only sound familiar but share the same spelling pattern. However, this is not always the case as sometimes the same sound can be spelt in different ways. For example, *'boast'*; *'toast'* rhyming with *'most'* and *'post'*. The sentence completion exercise requires the pupils to use seven out of the twelve words blended in exercise one. For exercises such as this, it is more effective if the pupil does the exercise orally first, and then writes the missing words from memory without looking at the word list above. The pupil can then check his/her own work by referring to the upper part of the worksheet.

Worksheet 3   st + suffixes

Pupils following a structured spelling programme will probably be familiar with the concept of suffixes and know something of the rules by which suffixes are added to base words. This worksheet reinforces the rule that base words ending in a consonant blend will just add the suffix. When most of these suffixes are added, an extra syllable is added to the word. (Pupils can count the beats by clapping or other means.) Adding suffix 's' to a base word ending in 'st' changes the sound of the end blend which loses its sharp /t/ sound. This is the only suffix which does not add another syllable to the word. For the sentence completion exercise, encourage pupils to tick each word as they use it. This will make it easier to complete the remaining sentences by process of elimination.

Worksheet 4   st

This worksheet focuses on the similar endings, words ending in the blend 'st' as in *'cost',* and words ending in 't' + suffix 's' as in *'cots'.* These endings not only look similar, but are very similar in sound. Pupils are asked to highlight the 'st' blends before reading the words. The suffix 's' in the remaining words could also be highlighted or circled in another colour. Some of the 'st' words also have suffix 's' added to them ('fists', 'tests', and 'vests'). Using different colours to highlight the blend and suffix in the same word will make it easier for the pupil to read these words and recognise the structure. The sentence reading exercise is mainly for fun, and to give further practice of the endings focused on. If the pupil copes well with reading the target words, s/he can be asked to spell a few of these words or write two or three of the easier sentences as a dictation.

Worksheet 5   st

There are quite a number of two-syllable words ending in 'st' of which the first syllable is a prefix. This worksheet focuses on a few of such words, and the first exercise requires the pupil to blend the prefix with the second syllable to make eight words. This demands a higher level of vocabulary than previous worksheets on 'st', but is a suitable task for older pupils. (Pupils might produce the word 'confest', mistaking it for 'confessed', and should be reminded that words ending in 'ss' + 'ed' suffix sound the same as words ending in the 'st' blend, for example, 'passed', 'missed'.) The sentence completion exercise should be done orally first, and the target words written without looking at the word list above. This can be used for checking purposes. For the second exercise, pupils should be asked which prefix is an open syllable (that is, 'rō') and the vowel marked long once this is identified. Pupils could be asked to write sentences of their own using the target words as a follow-up exercise.

Worksheet 6   sk

The blend 'sk' can also be used at the beginning of words (see *"Spotlight on Blends", Book One,* Worksheets 7a and 7b), but is more common as an end blend. Some of the words focused on in the word tracking exercise are ones which have 'a' in the middle with the long sound as in *'bath'* (for example, *'task'*, *'mask'*, *'bask'*). As pointed out in notes to Worksheet 1, dyslexics often use 'ar' to spell this sound in all conditions. They should be reminded that 'ar' is never used before an end blend. There is a short focus on two-syllable words with 'sk' in the middle following the word tracking exercise. The syllable structure of these words can be pointed out, and the pattern marked if pupils have been trained in coding words. The words *'musket'* and *'brisket'* may not be known by the pupils, and they should be encouraged to use a dictionary rather than just guessing.

Worksheet 7   sk   sp

The blend 'sp' is not very common, and in this worksheet is contrasted with 'sk'. Pupils should be told that the vowel 'a' can be pronounced like the 'a' in *'bath'* in words ending in these blends. (Target words include, *'mask'*, *'clasp'*, *'bask'*, *'grasp'* and *'task'*.) The word *'wasp'* is also included, and pupils might not be able to complete this word by phonic blending as they will not realise the 'a' sounds like 'o'. The vocabulary exercise aims to extend vocabulary by including the rather less common words *'husk'* and *'wisp'*.

Worksheet 8   st   sk

The end blends with 's' are easily confused, and this worksheet contrasts 'st' and 'sk'. The worksheet focuses on simple words, and would be suitable for younger pupils who have already practised these blends separately. The sentence completion exercise requires nine out of the possible twelve words to be used.

Worksheet 9   st   sk   sp

This worksheet and the next three are designed to contrast 'st', 'sk' and 'sp' which are difficult blends to distinguish. The worksheet is a straightforward onset-and-rime blending exercise. Each beginning can only blend with one of the target end blends. In the second exercise, several of the words can be completed with more than one vowel.

Worksheet 10   st   sk   sp

The format of this worksheet obviously makes it more suitable for the younger pupil. The balloons should be coloured according to the end blend of the word inside each balloon. (Pupils should be discouraged from colouring over the words themselves, as this could make them difficult to read.) Only nine out of the possible fourteen words are required for the sentence completion exercise. The words which are not needed are *'task'*, *'risk'*, *'grasp'*, *'disk'* and *'frost'*. A small tick can be put over the balloons containing words which do have to be used for the gap-filling exercise for pupils who might be confused by too many words.

Worksheet 11   st   sk   sp

This worksheet involves the completion of words in sentences, and if pupils have completed the previous worksheets on these blends they should recognise many of the same words. If the correct endings are written lightly in pencil first, each blend can then be traced over with a coloured pen, using a different colour for each blend. This will make the task of writing the words in the correct list easier. When doing this task, pupils should say the word aloud first, spell it by naming the letters, read it back and then check that it has been spelt correctly.

Worksheet 12   st   sk   sp

This worksheet is a rhyming practice sheet. It makes the assumption that pupils already know what a rhyme is, but they can be reminded that rhyming words sound the same in the middle and end, and in most cases will have the same spelling pattern. Distractors are built into each line of letters, so that pupils will have to pay very careful attention to the sequence of letters to find the rhyming word.

Worksheet 13   mp

The blend 'mp' is a fairly common one, and one which pupils in the earlier stages of literacy will need to be familiar with for both reading and spelling. Dyslexics often omit the 'm' when spelling words with this end blend. To make sure pupils can distinguish this end blend, they can be given orally a number of words ending in 'm', 'p' or 'mp' and asked to point to the correct ending written on the card. This worksheet involves the reading of words ending in 'mp' to identify real words as opposed to nonsense words. The reading of nonsense words requires the pupil to decode phonologically without the aid of visual recall. Younger pupils might need a little help for the wordsearch activity. The target words could actually be given to pupils. They would then have to find them in the word square and match them to the meanings.

Worksheet 14   mp

This worksheet uses rhyming words to trigger 'mp' words to match given meanings. Pupils might not know *'clump'* and *'ramp'*, but should be able to find the rest of the words quite easily. The exercise requiring pupils to write out the rhyming words can be done from memory to make it more challenging, though a realistic target would be for pupils to remember three words rhyming with *'lamp'* and *'jump'*, and one word to rhyme with *'limp'*.

Worksheet 15   nd

The blend 'nd' is a very common one, and pupils will already have met it in simple words such as *'and'*, *'hand'*, *'mend'*, and so on. It causes most problems for spelling, dyslexics tending to miss out the letter 'n'. A useful sound discrimination exercise is to present the pupils with pairs of words which differ only in their endings, for example, *'had'*, *'hand'*, *'sad'*, *'sand'*, etc., and ask them to identify which word in each pair they can hear. The first exercise on the worksheet focuses on reading accuracy. The second exercise highlights the small group of 'nd' words with long 'ī' in the middle. Pupils should be alerted to the sound pattern as well as the visual one. The words *'hind'* and *'grind'* might be unfamiliar to some pupils, but this is a way of extending vocabulary. The last sentence has two missing words, but as only two words will be left for filling the blanks, the solution should be obvious.

Worksheet 16   nd

The first exercise is an onset-and-rime blending exercise which includes words with 'ou' in the middle. Pupils should be alerted to the long 'ī' sound in 'mī' and 'rī' which make the words *'mind'* and *'rind'* respectively. The rhyming pairs needed to complete each sentence are:

1	found	ground		4	sand	hand
2	send	mend		5	bond	fond
3	mind	rind		6	pound	round

Worksheet 17   nt

The blend 'nt' is also a very common one, and one in which the /n/ sound is often omitted in spelling. The first exercise focuses on reading accuracy. The idea of putting nonsense words in the bin appeals to younger pupils. In the sentence reading exercise, the pupil has to choose the correct alternative between words which are visually very similar, with only one element of the word distinguishing it from the other. Pupils could be asked to spell some of the 'nt' words as a follow-up exercise to the worksheet.

Worksheet 18   nt

This is a straightforward worksheet which most pupils should be able to do fairly independently. There is some incidental practice of initial consonant blends in the first exercise, including the three consonant blends 'spl' and 'spr'. Distractors are built into the word tracking exercise, so pupils will have to make use of contextual clues in the sentences to find the correct word. (Younger pupils might not know the word *'flint'* in sentence number 4, although the letter sequence makes this the only likely word.)

Worksheet 19   nd   nt

This is the first worksheet to contrast the similar blends 'nd' and 'nt'. Pupils are required to choose the correct end blend for each beginning. The format of the worksheet with the net for 'nd' words on the left might cause directional difficulties when blending the words. It is therefore suggested that the end blends 'nd' and 'nt' are written on a small card as shown below which can be slid into position as the pupil does the sound blending task. The beginning letter combination which can be blended with both 'nd' and 'nt' is 'spe'.

nd
nt

Worksheet 20   nd   nt

This worksheet requires pupils to complete words in sentences with the correct end blend. If the endings are first written in pencil, they can then be traced over in colour pen, a different colour for each blend. This will make the second task easier when the pupil is required to write each word in the correct list. Pupils should verbalise the words before writing them from memory, naming each letter as they spell the word, and reading the complete word once they have written it. The words to be completed are mostly one-syllable words with short vowels, although the word 'invented' has been included (sentence 3), as well as words with 'ou' in the middle in the last sentence.

Worksheet 21   nd   nt

This is a rhyming practice sheet similar in format to Worksheet 12. The target words include words with long and short vowels, as well as vowel digraphs 'ai', 'ou' and 'oi'. Pupils could be asked to think of further rhyming words for some of the words, for example, *'land'* or *'kind'* for which there are several rhyming words. (This activity can be enlivened by the teacher thinking of a given rhyming word first, and asking the pupil to guess what this is by giving a loose definition.)

Worksheet 22   nd   nt

The suffix 'ed' needs particular attention on a structured spelling course since it can have three different sounds depending on the base word. When 'ed' is added to a base word ending in 'nd' or 'nt', an extra syllable is added. (Pupils should be asked to count the beats by clapping or other means.) The gap filling exercise is straightforward as only one word is missing from each sentence except for the last sentence. Again, pupils can be encouraged to do this exercise orally first, and to write the answers from memory, checking that they have spelt the words correctly after they have completed the exercise.

Worksheet 23a and 23b   nd   nt

These worksheets focus on longer words ending in 'nd' or 'nt' of which the first element is a prefix. These words make excellent practice for syllable recognition and pupils should be asked to identify each prefix as an open or closed syllable. The worksheets can also be viewed as an opportunity to extend vocabulary with less common words such as *'expend'* or *'expand'*. They also give pupils the opportunity to write their own sentences. In sentence number 4 on Worksheet 23a, the sentence could be completed by either *'expand'* or *'extend'*. In Worksheet 23b, one of the target words in the syllable blending exercise is *'present'* as a verb with the stress on the final syllable. (The syllable structure for *'present'* as a noun with stress on the first syllable can be discussed with the pupil if appropriate, as these two words make an interesting comparison in that they look identical, but are pronounced differently.)

Worksheet 24   -ump   -unt

This worksheet contrasts end blends 'mp' and 'nt' which are sometimes confused owing to similarity in sounds, namely a nasal sound followed by a plosive sound. The context clues in the sentences should make the task of choosing the correct ending easier. The wordsearch adds an element of fun to the worksheet, as well as practising visual discrimination skills. In the word square, the word *'lump'* has its own position in the square (first line going across) even though it is also found inside the word *'slump'* and *'plump'*.

Worksheet 25   nd   nt   mp

This worksheet consists of a straightforward onset-and-rime sound blending task, contrasting the end blends 'nd', 'nt' and 'mp'. Each end blend has to be used three times. In the second exercise, each beginning can blend with two possible endings.

Worksheet 26   nd   nt   mp

This worksheet is identical in format to number 10 and the same guidelines apply. The four words in the balloons which are not needed for the sentence completion exercise are *'plant'*, *'jump'*, *'damp'* and *'hunt'*.

Worksheet 27   ng

Only one sound is represented by the letters 'ng' (the phonetic symbol is /ŋ/) and therefore this is a consonant digraph rather than a blend. However, it is included because visually it looks like the other consonant blends and is an important sound which needs to be introduced and practised in the early stages of a reading and spelling programme. This sound also constitutes the first element of the consonant blend 'nk'. The format of this worksheet is identical to Worksheet 17, and the same guidelines apply. The sentences employ simple vocabulary and spelling patterns and could perhaps be used for dictation if appropriate.

Worksheet 28   ng

This worksheet is identical in format to number 18. Several of the words in the first exercise can be completed with more than one short vowel. In sentence number 3, pupils might not know the word *'rung'* meaning step on a ladder, but can be asked to guess from the line of letters what the word is. (The sequence of letters can generate *'spung'*, *'pung'*, *'gang'*, *'frung'* or *'rung'* as possible words.)

Worksheet 29   ng

The sound /ŋ/ is contained within the suffix 'ing', one of the most common suffixes. This worksheet focuses on a selection of base words ending in 'ng' to which suffix 'ing' is then added. The gap filling exercise is straightforward but will be more effective if done orally first and the answers written from memory with spellings checked after the whole exercise is completed.

Worksheet 30   nk

This worksheet introduces the important blend 'nk' which is also of high frequency. The onset-and-rime sound blending exercise requires the pupils to find four words ending in 'ank', 'ink' and 'unk' respectively, which then have to be written in the correct list. The vocabulary exercise is not connected to the first exercise. The words chosen should be known to most pupils, with the possible exception of *'mink'*. If this worksheet is being done with a small group of pupils, each can be asked to give a definition for another 'nk' word which the other pupils then have to guess.

Worksheet 31   nk

This worksheet gives further sound blending practice of words ending in 'nk' in the first exercise. (Several words can be completed by more than one short vowel.) The second exercise requires sentences to be completed with the correct 'nk' word. Pupils should be told to tick each word once it has been used so that it becomes easier to fill the remaining blanks by process of elimination.

Worksheet 32   ng   nk

This is the first of several worksheets which contrast the similar endings 'ng' and 'nk'. Generally, these need quite a lot of practice as confusions often occur. The format of this worksheet will make it more appealing to younger pupils. When the pupil finds a target word in the square, he/she should be asked to write it on the line below the relevant picture, otherwise it will be hard to do the alphabetical sequencing exercise which follows.

Worksheet 33   ng   nk

This is another worksheet aimed at younger pupils which contrasts 'ng' and 'nk'. This time, the pupil has to spell ten words ending in either 'ng' or 'nk' which will be read to him/her. (Teachers can make their own selection of words.) It might be necessary to do a quick auditory discrimination exercise before the spelling to ensure that the pupil can distinguish the endings. The sentence completion exercise forces pupils to pay attention to context in order to decide which words must be chosen from the alternatives given.

Worksheet 34   ng   nk

This worksheet is identical in format to number 19, and it is suggested that a small card with the endings 'ng' and 'nk' is used for the initial onset-and-rime blending exercise. The beginning which can blend with both endings is 'ba'. In the sentence writing exercise, more able pupils can be asked to include two of the target words in each sentence. Pupils can also be asked to identify which of the target words in the first exercise have more than one meaning (that is, *'bank'*, *'spring'*, *'long'*).

Worksheet 35   ng   nk

This worksheet requires the completion of words in sentences with the correct ending. It should not take long for the worksheet to be completed, and some of the sentences could be used for dictation as an optional follow-up.

Worksheet 36   -ing   -ink

This worksheet involves completing words with the missing rime, either '-ing' or '-ink'. The wordsearch provides a fun element which will appeal to younger pupils. As for the previous worksheet, two or three of the shorter sentences could be given for dictation after the worksheet has been completed successfully. Pupils can also be asked to recall as many of the '-ing' and '-ink' words as possible as an optional memory exercise.

Worksheet 37a and 37b   ng   nk

These worksheets involve blending the beginning, middle and end sounds in order to make words ending in 'ng' or 'nk'. Only two middle vowel sounds are used in each blending exercise which reduces the complexity of the task. In Worksheet 37a, target words include *'rung'*, *'rank'* and *'hunk'* which might not be known by some pupils, but the meaning can be deduced from the sentences in which these words are used. The four remaining words to be used in sentences of the pupils' own making are *'hang'*, *'bang'*, *'bank'* and *'thank'*. As these are common words, pupils should be able to incorporate them into sentences without too much difficulty. In Worksheet 37b the target words should not cause confusion, with the possible exception of the word *'mink'*. In the gap filling exercise, each sentence has two gaps which makes the sentence completion task more challenging.

Worksheet 38   ng   nk

This worksheet is similar to rhyming practice sheets numbers 12 and 21, although in the worksheet the pupil is required to find two words which rhyme with the word inside the box. There is also a follow-up memory exercise which pupils might enjoy as an added challenge.

Worksheet 39   mp   ng   nk

This worksheet contrasts the endings 'mp', 'ng' and 'nk', and provides useful consolidation once these sounds have been practised separately. As for other worksheets of this format, some of the sentences can also be used for dictation as an optional follow-up.

Worksheet 40   nch

The first exercise involves choosing the correct short vowel to complete each word. In some cases, more than one choice is possible (for example, 'b__nch', 'p__nch'). In 'branch', the vowel sound is not short /ă/, although the colloquial word 'brunch' can also be made using short /ŭ/. The level of vocabulary makes this worksheet more suitable for older pupils, and some help might be needed to complete the less common words such as 'stench', 'wrench', 'winch' and 'flinch'. The suffixing exercise focuses on the suffixes 'es' and 'ed'. It is assumed that pupils will already know the rule concerning use of suffix 'es' instead of 's', but this is a good opportunity to remind pupils that words ending in 'ch' take this suffix. When the suffix 'ed' is added to words ending in 'nch', the sound is /t/. This also needs to be pointed out to dyslexic pupils who often spell the 'ed' suffix as it sounds. As for other gap filling exercises, pupils should be encouraged to work out the answers orally first, and then write the answers without looking at the target words. Pupils can then check their own answers.

Worksheet 41   nge

It is assumed that pupils already know that 'ge' makes a /j/ sound at the end of words, and will be familiar with words such as 'stage' and 'rage'. The blend 'nge' with the nasal sound before the final /j/ sound is one which needs specific practice. The first exercise includes both two-syllable words, as well as a few less common words which pupils might need help with, for example, 'tinge', 'lunge', 'binge', 'cringe' and 'whinge'. In this exercise, a few of the words have to be completed with the long /ā/ sound, for example, 'change', 'arrange', 'range', 'strange', and 'grange'. Pupils can be asked to find these words first, and to complete the remaining words with short vowels. The other exercises on the worksheet involve vocabulary tasks, and focus on the 'nge' blend in the middle of words before endings such as 'er' and 'y'.

Worksheet 42   nce

This worksheet gives practice in the end blend 'nce' in the form of vocabulary questions in which pupils have to find rhyming words ending in 'nce' to match a given meaning. It is assumed that pupils are already familiar with 'ce' at the end of words with the soft sound as in *'face'*, *'mice'*, and so on. Pupils seem to enjoy the challenge of vocabulary quizzes such as these, and should be able to answer most of the questions independently. In less common words of more than one syllable, the first syllable is given, as for *'enhance'*, *'convince'* and *'announce'*. In the case of more difficult words such as these, the teacher could give one or two more letters as a clue. The answers are given below:

DANCE	1	France	5	chance	SINCE	1	prince	3	wince
	2	glance	6	stance		2	mince	4	convince
	3	trance	7	prance					
	4	enhance	8	lance					

DISTANCE	1	entrance	3	balance	FLOUNCE	1	ounce	3	pounce
	2	instance				2	announce	4	bounce

Worksheet 43   ance

The following two worksheets focus on the difficult endings 'ance' and 'ence', and are designed for older, secondary school pupils or adults who already have a grasp of basic grammatical categories such as parts of speech. It is also assumed that pupils know the basic suffixing rules such changing 'y' to 'i' as in *'defiance'*. This worksheet only focuses on a few words ending in 'ance'. Pupils should be encouraged to make their own reference list of these words as they are so easily confused with words ending in 'ence'.

Worksheet 44   ence

This worksheet complements the previous one on words ending in 'ance', and is of the same level of difficulty. The format is similar for the first two exercises, but includes a vocabulary quiz for the third exercise. Pupils might like to include some of the target words in sentences of their own.

Worksheet 45   nch   nge   nce

This worksheet contrasts the very similar end blends 'nch', 'nge' and 'nce' where the nasal sound /n/ is before the final consonant sound. The onset of each word in the first exercise can only blend with one rime, and the words are all fairly simple ones. The contextual clues in the word completion exercises should ensure a high level of success in the second exercise.

Worksheet 46   ft

By completing the wordsearch, pupils should end up with a list of the most common words ending in 'ft' which is not a very common end blend, but includes some words of high frequency such as *'gift'*, *'soft'* and *'left'*. Dyslexic pupils sometimes spell this blend 'fed' instead of 'ft', confusing it with suffix 'ed' which often has a /t/ sound. Pupils might need to be given the first letter of words which are less common such as *'tuft'* or *'shaft'*. The answers are given below:

1	gift	6	shift	10	craft
2	drift	7	lift	11	swift
3	soft	8	draft	12	shaft
4	left	9	tuft	13	graft
5	loft				

Worksheet 47   ff   ft

This worksheet contrasts the similar endings 'ff' and 'ft'. Confusion can arise when the suffix 'ed' is attached to a word ending in 'ff' as in *'sniffed'* because the final sound will be identical to the 'ft' blend. (Other words ending in 'ff' which can take 'ed' suffix are *'huff'*, *'puff'*, *'stuff'*, *'bluff'* and *'scoff'*. A special focus on these words could be introduced in conjunction with this worksheet.)

Worksheet 48   ld

This is the first of several worksheets involving 'l' blends. Words ending in the blend 'ld' are generally preceded by a long vowel, and in this worksheet pupils are required to find the correct rhyming word according to meanings given. Most of the target words should be known by even younger pupils with the possible exceptions of *'mild'* and *'scald'*. (Pupils should be explicitly told that the spelling choice 'ld' is preceded by a long vowel, as short vowels followed by the same sound are base words ending in 'll' with 'ed' suffix such as *'killed'*, *'filled'*, etc. The only 'ld' word with a short vowel is *'held'*.)

Worksheet 49   lt

Words ending in 'lt' are generally preceded by a short vowel. The words in the first exercise are less common than those to be found in the word square, and the first exercise lends itself to dictionary work. It can be pointed out that the word *'jolt'* is a little unusual in that it has a long /ō/ sound. (Other 'lt' words which rhyme with it are *'bolt'* and *'colt'*, although not included in this worksheet.)

Worksheet 50   ld   lt

This worksheet contrasts the similar end blends 'ld' and 'lt'. Before doing the onset-and-rime exercise, it might be advisable to mark the vowels long or short to encourage sound blending rather than choosing the ending which just looks right. Context should make it easy for the pupil to choose the correct words in the second exercise. The sentences can be used for dictation as a follow-up.

Worksheet 51   ld   lt

This is another worksheet contrasting 'ld' and 'lt'. Once again, it might be useful to mark the vowels long or short in the incomplete words as most pupils will assume that the vowel is short. In fact, several of the target words contain long vowels.

Worksheet 52   lk   lp   lb

This worksheet brings together the end blends 'lk', 'lp' and 'lb', which are not common. In fact, the word *'bulb'* is the only one which has this ending. The worksheet includes a visual discrimination exercise as well as the more familiar onset-and-rime exercise. The beginning which can have two endings is *'bu'* which makes *'bulk'* and *'bulb'*. (In connection with words ending in 'lk', teachers might like to mention words like *'talk'*, *'walk'*, etc., which look like *'milk'*, *'sulk'*, etc., but where the 'l' is silent.)

Worksheet 53   lk   lt   lk   lp   lf

Words with 'l' blends are often misread by dyslexics who transpose letters, for example, reading *'sold'* as *'slod'*. This worksheet brings together all the end blends with 'l', and requires the pupil to scan along the line of letters to find words which match the given word in the box.

Worksheet 54a and 54b   lf

Words ending in 'lf' are not very common, and the first exercise covers the most common ones. However, a separate exercise is given on words which are made with *'self'*, including the plural form *'selves'*. Pupils should be reminded that these words are written as one, and not separately. Words ending in 'lf' which change to 'lves' in the plural are focused on in Worksheet 54b as it seemed appropriate to link these words with the plural form of *'self'*.

Worksheet 55   lve   lge

The blend 'lve' is found at the end of a few words in addition to the plural form of words ending in 'lf'. In the syllable blending exercise, it is useful to remind pupils that 'e' and 're' are open syllables and that the vowel is therefore long. The word structure of *'dissolve'* can also be commented on, namely that it has a double 's' in the middle because the first 's' belongs to the prefix 'dis', while the second one belongs to the second syllable 'solve'. The blend 'lge' is very uncommon, and is only given a brief focus.

Worksheet 56   ct

The end blend 'ct' is fairly common in longer words of Latin origin, and is often spelt incorrectly as the /t/ element is not always picked up, and sometimes 'ck' is used instead of 'ct'. Words ending in 'ct' lend themselves to work on syllable division, and therefore the first two exercises in both this worksheet and number 57 are syllable blending exercises. Pupils should be reminded of the difference between open and closed syllables prior to doing these exercises, so that long vowels are read correctly.

Worksheet 57   ct

This worksheet gives further practice of words ending in 'ct', and follows a similar format to number 56. The same guidelines apply. The prefix 'in' can blend with *'flect'*, *'tact'* and *'dict'*. It is assumed pupils will not be familiar with words such as *'inflect'* or *'indict'*, but will hopefully know *'intact'*.

Worksheet 58   pt

This worksheet focuses on one-syllable words ending in the blend 'pt'. There are only a few of these words, four of which are past tense verbs. The endings of words like *'ripped'*, *'stepped'* etc. will also sound like the blend 'pt', and these words are more common than the few ending in the blend 'pt'. The last exercise on the worksheet highlights this fact, and requires pupils to notice the structure of such words. It is assumed that they will already have been taught the doubling rule. (Other words of the same pattern are *'clip'*, *'clap'*, *'dip'*, *'flop'*, *'lap'*, *'mop'*, *'nip'*, *'step'*, *'stop' and 'slip'*.)

Worksheet 59   pt

This worksheet focuses on two-syllable words ending in 'pt' which begin with prefixes. Pupils should be alerted to the instruction that one prefix has to be used twice in each exercise in order to make five words. The level of vocabulary makes this worksheet suitable for older pupils who need more advanced spelling practice and vocabulary extension. There is also a short focus on four words ending in the difficult blend 'mpt' which lends itself to dictionary practice.